NI PRESS PRESENTS   **BRYAN LEE O'MALLEY'S**

IN HIS FINEST HOUR

John Kantz art assistant
Aaron Ancheta junior assistant
Ben Berntsen back cover art
Dylan McCrae cover colors
Bryan Lee O'Malley and **Keith Wood** book design
James Lucas Jones editor

First edition: July 2010
ISBN: 978-1-934964-38-5

Published by **Oni Press, Inc.**

Joe Nozemack publisher | **James Lucas Jones** editor in chief
Cory Casoni marketing director | **Keith Wood** art director
George Rohac operations director | **Jill Beaton** associate editor
Charlie Chu associate editor | **Douglas E. Sherwood** production assistant

3 4 5 6 7 8 9 10
www.onipress.com | www.scottpilgrim.com | www.radiomaru.com
PRINTED IN THE U.S.A. by Lake Book Manufacturing.

ONI PRESS, INC.
1305 SE Martin Luther King Jr. Blvd.
Suite A
Portland, OR 97214
USA

WHAT? HE GAVE IT TO ME. YOUNG NEIL. HE'S *NICE.*

HE GAVE IT TO YOU.

...FOR $200.

SO I WAS GOING TO DO YOU A FAVOUR AND MAKE DINNER, BUT IT APPEARS THAT ALL YOU HAVE IN THE HOUSE IS RAMEN NOODLES AND CEREAL.

...THE ECONOMY...

FWUMP

ANYWAY, LET'S GO OUT! *CHICKEN WINGS.* I'LL HOOK YOU UP. WE'LL GO TO HOOTERS. IT'S YOUR FAVOURITE!

WHAP

HOOTERS IS *YOUR* FAVOURITE.

SERIOUSLY.

GET OUT OF THE HOUSE. GO MEET WOMEN.

SOME OTHER NIGHT

REMEMBER HOW YOU BROKE YOUR BASS? LIKE... 4 MONTHS AGO?

I DON'T THINK IT WAS 4 MONTHS AGO.

ANYWAY, WE'RE PLAYING AT CAMERON HOUSE ON MONDAY, AND, I MEAN, YOU COULD COME.

...SCOTT.

OH DUDE, I FINALLY BEAT THIS— THIS ONE GUY...

I BEAT THIS ONE GUY... VIDEO GAMES...

16

DOES THAT MEAN YOU WERE PRACTICALLY SIXTEEN WHEN WE MET?

SKOOCH
SKOOCH

NO WAY! WE MET ON MY SEVENTEENTH BIRTHDAY, SILLY!

SO... UH... HOW'S IT FEEL TO BE... UH... NO LONGER A CHILD IN THE EYES OF THE LAW?

SKETCHY-ASS 24-YEAR-OLD

AW... IT'S OKAY.

BUH?

I'M MOVING *AWAY* SOON! I APPLIED TO MCGILL AND UBC AND I'M *GRADUATING* IN *THREE MONTHS!!!*

SO THAT HAPPENED.

I'M TRULY FLATTERED BY YOUR DELIGHTFUL OFFER, BUT LET'S TRY TO BE GROWNUPS HERE, OKAY?

IT'S WALLACE'S FAULT! HE GAVE ME CONFUSING ADVICE! HOW I HATE HIM.

YEAH...

SCOTT, DO YOU REMEMBER HOW YOU, LIKE, CHEATED ON ME AND STUFF? KIND OF A CRUMMY BOYFRIEND, IN RETROSPECT?

I... UHH... SORT OF...

scotty ur so hot & sexxy

o hey thanx

MEMORY CAM

30

SCOTT, I DON'T *WANT* YOU ANYMORE.

IT DOESN'T MEAN I DON'T LOVE YOU.

BUT... I'VE MOVED ON.

YOU LIKE STEPHEN STILLS, DON'T YOU?

STEPHEN? PSSHHAHA HAHA

WHY IS THAT FUNNY?

I'M HAPPY BEING ALONE RIGHT NOW, SCOTT. I'M TRYING TO LEARN TO LIKE ME. *ALONE.*

I MEAN, I'VE SPENT A YEAR OF MY LIFE ON YOU!

A YEAR!

BUT...

...IT'S COOL IF WE JUST MAKE OUT FOR A WHILE.

SMOOCH!

BUT IT WAS HORRIBLE

FOR EVERYONE

AND THAT INCLUDES YOU

33 She says what she means

WHERE YOU BEEN? I DIDN'T KNOW YOU KNEW SARAH JANE.

WHO THE HELL IS SARAH JANE?

THIS IS HER PARTY, MAN.

IT'S HER BIRTHDAY.

...WHAT AM I DOING HERE?

I THOUGHT THIS WAS A JULIE PARTY.

JULIE MOVED TO MONTREAL.

YOUNG NEIL (NOT REALLY VERY YOUNG)

WHAT?!

I HEARD ENVY ADAMS WAS HERE.

ENVY ADAMS? NO WAY!

APPARENTLY SHE LOOKS *AMAZING*.

OH MAN! I'M TOTALLY GAY FOR HER.

MONIQUE AGAIN?

SANDRA LIKE, WHAT THE HELL

WHAT THE *HELL*, YOUNG NEIL. IS THIS TRUE?

SHE *DOES* LOOK AMAZING. YOU SHOULD JUST, LIKE, PREEMPTIVELY BE A DICK TO HER, MAN.

REALLY? THAT WORKS?

ENVY ADAMS? PARTYING WITH *MERE MORTALS?*

NICE TO SEE YOU AGAIN, SCOTT.

WHISPER WHISPER
WHISPER GASP! UGH! WHISPER

UM... WHAT ARE YOU DRINKING? LET ME BUY YOU A...

JEEZ...

UM, I'M SORRY, I....

WE'LL SPARE YOU THE EMBARRASSMENT OF WITNESSING THE REST OF THIS AWFUL SPECTACLE.

(TURN THE PAGE)

VERY MATURE, SCOTT.

LIKE YOU ACTUALLY CARE.

OF COURSE I CARE. DON'T BE A BABY.

POUT

YOU MAKE ME OUT TO BE SOME KIND OF *VILLAINESS.* WE WERE PRACTICALLY *KIDS* WHEN WE DATED, SCOTT, AND IT'S NOT LIKE *YOU* WERE SOME PARAGON OF VIRTUE.

I WAS *SUCH A* PARAGON.

CHUG

AND.

I WAS *SUCH A* PARAGON!

OVER IT.

WHAT IS THE *DEAL* WITH HER, MAN?? I SWEAR TO GOD!! SHE'S GOT SINISTER MOTIVES OR SOMETHING! GIDEON SENT HER TO MESS WITH MY HEAD!!

SHE'S THE DEVIL, SCOTT.

(HE HAD COFFEE)

GIDEON'S PROBABLY IN TOWN, TOO! THEY'RE IN *CAHOOTS*, MAN!! WHAT THE HELL DO I *DO*??

OF COURSE HE'S IN TOWN. DIDN'T YOU READ THE ARTICLE I SHOWED YOU?

OH MAN! MAYBE SHE WANTS TO GET BACK TOGETHER!

PSSH. SHE'S SCREWING GIDEON, OBVIOUSLY.

HM... NO, RAMONA'S SCREWING GIDEON...

WELL, THE THREE OF THEM CAN ALL SCREW, CAN'T THEY?

SO LIKE, ME AND ENVY ARE LIKE 24 NOW, RIGHT?

SHE'S 25. HER BIRTHDAY WAS IN FEBRUARY.

WHAT? HOW DO YOU KNOW?

IT WAS A BIG DEAL, GUY.

I READ ABOUT THE PARTY IN ITALIAN *VOGUE*. I THINK DAVID BOWIE WAS THERE.

OK, BUT WE'RE GROWING UP A BIT, RIGHT?? WE'RE MOVING ON!!

MOVING ON TO THREE-SOMES WITH GIDEON AND RAMONA.

SALE! TAKE OUR BOOKS - PLEASE

AND THEN WALLACE BOUGHT HIM SUSHI.

MM! IT'S GOOD!

THAT NIGHT

MESSAGE WRITING

ONE NEW MESSAGE.

4:18 PM.

WHUMP

WHRRI

↑ON

HEY. IT'S KIM.

I JUST SAW A GUY WITH A PARKA EXACTLY LIKE YOUR STUPID PARKA YOU'VE HAD SINCE YOU WERE 12.

THAT'S LITERALLY THE MOST INTERESTING THING THAT'S HAPPENED ALL WEEK. IT FRIGGIN' SUCKS UP HERE.

GET OVER YOUR EXTREMELY BORING DEPRESSION AND COME VISIT ME SOMETIME, ASS-CLOWN.

CLICK

THE
NEXT
DAY...

WE WENT BOWLING AT MIDNIGHT. JULIE AND STEPHEN BAKED ME A TERRIBLE CAKE.

YOU GOT PRETTY DRUNK.

I DON'T DRINK.

MM-HMM.

SO DO YOU THINK WE'RE GOING TO GET BACK TOGETHER?

HUH? WHAT, ME AND YOU?

OR MAYBE JUST HAVE *CASUAL SEX?*

• • • •

EMORY CAM

WHAT ABOUT NEW YEAR'S EVE? DO YOU REMEMBER THAT?

WE HAD A FIGHT.

LIKE A *FIGHT* FIGHT?

A FIGHT THAT *YOU* STARTED.

WELL, I REMEMBER YOU *BREAKING* MY HEART.

THE FEELING IS SOMEWHAT MUTUAL.

I KNOW I'M CHANGING. WE'RE ALL CHANGING.

JUST... DON'T FORGET ME.

THIS IS THE ONLY ME *HE* KNOWS...

YOU NEED TO FACE REALITY, SCOTT.

HE'S NOT EVEN A BAD *GUY.*

h w o o o o o o o o o

GET ON THE BUS. YOU'RE LEAVING.

I DON'T UNDERSTAND WHAT'S HAPPENING!

DUNDAS STREET COACH TERMINAL

THINK OF IT AS A WILDERNESS SABBATICAL. GO. CLEANSE YOUR MIND.

THEN COME BACK AND FIGHT GIDEON.

WHAT?! I DON'T WANT TO FIGHT HIM!

SHUT UP. GO TRAIN.

I HAVE NO REASON TO FIGHT HIM!!

THE
GREAT WHITE
NORTH

34 A link to the past

AND IT'LL NEVER HAPPEN AGAIN.

87

SCOTT PILGRIM IS COMING HOME...

Toronto 80

...AND THIS TIME, IT'S PERSONAL!!

MMM... I DUNNO.

MAYBE LOSE THE SHOULDERS.

GIDEON GRAVES (31 YEARS OLD)

OCCUPATION: **ASSHOLE**

I WANT SOME OPTIONS ON THE SHOES.

AND HAIR, PEOPLE, MY GOD. *PLEASE.* I WANT YOU TO BUILD A BONFIRE IN HER HAIR. THAT IS A METAPHOR.

BACKSTAGE

NATALIE. IT'S YOUR *DEBUT*.

IT'S THE OPENING OF MY SPECIAL PLACE IN TORONTO. YOUR OUTFIT IS *IMPORTANT*.

I'VE HAD SOME VERY PROMISING YOUNG DESIGNERS *LITERALLY* CHAINED TO SEWING MACHINES FOR A MONTH.

AND YOU *KNOW* THAT DRESSING YOU UP LIKE A DOLL IS VERY FULFILLING FOR ME SEXUALLY.

SEEMS LIKE IT'S ABOUT THE *ONLY* THING.

WHAT WAS THAT?

NOTHING.

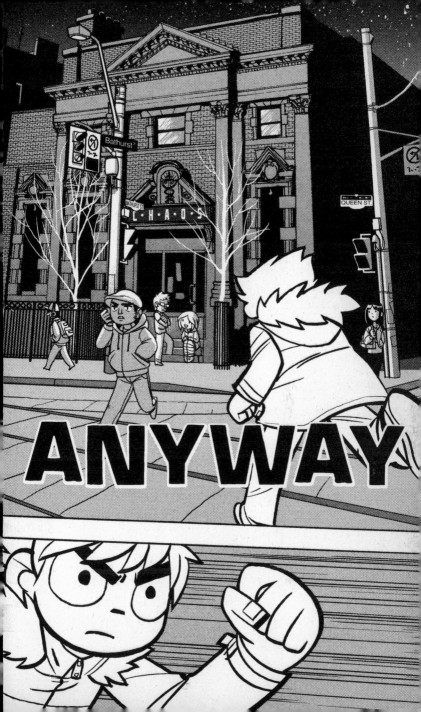

IT'S SEVEN DOLLARS, JOSEPH. I'LL HOLD MY COAT.

QUIT ACTING LIKE A BROKE-ASS BITCH.

GIVE ME SOMETHING WITH ICE IN IT. AND BOOZE.

BOOZE AND ICE, PLEASE.

GRIP

SIP

I... JULIE... YOU... I... MONTREAL...

UHH...

YOU'RE A MESS, MAN. WOULD YOU *LOOK* AT YOURSELF?

DURR?

WHYYYYYYY

HEY.

I GOT A FEW OF THESE LEFT. VIRAL MARKETING.

SAD.

NICE SHIRT, SCOTT!

STACEY PILGRIM
(LONG-SUFFERING YOUNGER SISTER)

SHUT UP. I SPILLED MY DRINK.

HAVE YOU SEEN RAMONA?

THE RAMONA WHO BROKE YOUR HEART AND RUINED YOUR LIFE AND HAD A THREE-SOME WITH THIS GIDEON CLOWN?

YOU NEED TO STOP TALKING TO WALLACE, OKAY?

ANYWAY, I THOUGHT YOU DIDN'T DRINK!!!

TIME CRITICS

OH... HEY, MAN.

UH-HUH.

PEW PEW

YOUNG NEIL

PEW

WAIT, DO YOU TWO NOT KNOW EACH OTHER? THAT'S CRAZY!

SCOTT'S SISTER, RIGHT?

NUH-UH.

PEW PEW

YEAH, HI.

STACEY, THIS IS YOUNG—

—THIS IS, UM, NEIL.

NEIL

This is the greatest day of his life.

ANYWAY.

SCOTT! HEY!

NICE SHIRT!

TAMARA (HER BEST FRIEND)

KNIVES (18 YEARS OLD)

UH... YEAH HOW'S IT GOING?

GREAT!

AWESOME!!

HEY, HAVE YOU GUYS SEEN—

YES!! I TOTALLY SAW ENVY ADAMS!! I MEAN I THINK I DID! IT LOOKED JUST LIKE HER!!

DID YOU LIKE HER SOLO ALBUM?

AREN'T WE AT THE RELEASE PARTY FOR IT?

PLEASE, IT LEAKED MONTHS AGO.

OH...

I HAVEN'T SEEN RAMONA, OR GIDEON GRAVES, OR—

KACHUNK

EEEEEEE!!!

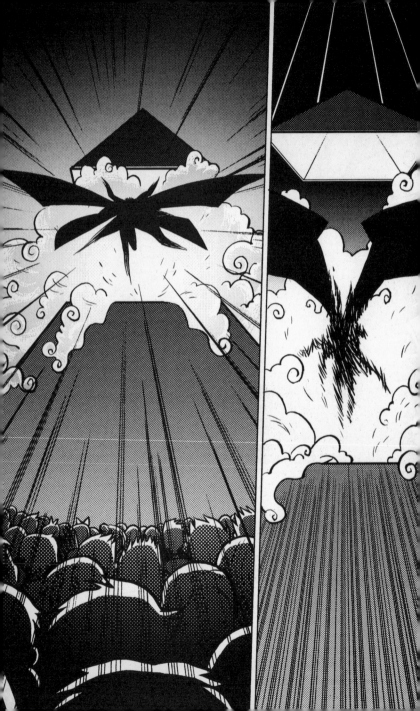

YOU'RE GIDEON?

SCOTT PILGRIM. CAN I JUST BE THE FIRST TO SAY... NICE SHIRT.

WHAT?

SHUT UP! YOU'RE LIKE THE THIRD PERSON TO SAY THAT!

I HAVEN'T LAID A FINGER ON HER, AMIGO. SHE'S PROBABLY IN THE LADIES' ROOM.

WHAT? RAMONA, DUDE.

WAIT. WHAT?

YOU... YOU DON'T HAVE HER?

...SHE ISN'T WITH YOU?

I PLANNED THIS THROUGH TO THE END ASSUMING YOU'D AT LEAST BE *COMPETENT* ENOUGH TO *KEEP HER AROUND!*

YOU DEFEATED *SIX* OF HER EVIL EX-BOYFRIENDS AND SHE *LEFT* YOU?!

SHUT UP! IT'S COMPLICATED!

IT'S QUITE *SIMPLE,* ACTUALLY!

DEAD

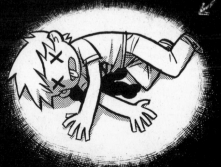

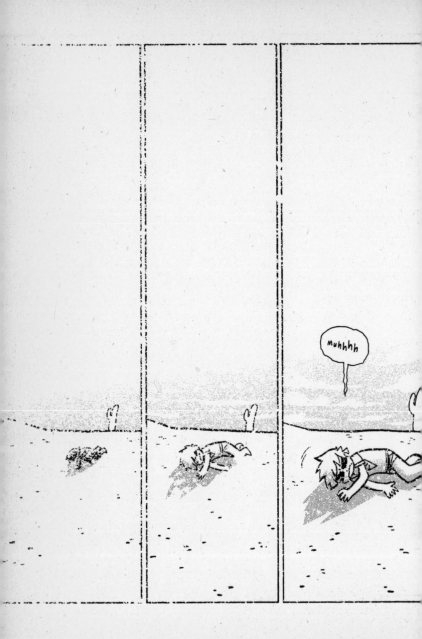

WELL, AT LEAST YOU WEREN'T WITH *HIM.*

GIDEON, I MEAN.

THAT ASS.

I'M SORRY.

I'M SORRY I LEFT. THOSE LAST FEW DAYS... I WAS PRETTY MESSED UP.

I DIDN'T WANT YOU TO GET MESSED UP TOO.

I GOT KINDA MESSED UP ANYWAY.

BUT... YOU'RE SO TOUGH.

...TO ADMIT THAT I WAS A CRUMMY GIRLFRIEND AND I FEEL LIKE AN IDIOT FOR EVEN TRYING TO—

SSHHHHHH

GAAAASP

SCOTT HAD AN EXTRA LIFE!

the beginning

YOU'RE NOT FROM AROUND HERE.

YOUR EYES...

THEY'VE SEEN THINGS.

YOU IDIOT.

I'M ALL-POWERFUL IN HER HEAD, MAN!

DID YOU THINK I'D JUST ROLL OVER IN HERE?

Music sounds better with you

38

209

CLOSURE

OH, MAN. WERE YOU AND GIDEON, LIKE, A THING?

WE COULD HAVE BEEN, BUT I DOUBT HE EVER FELT THAT WAY.

MAYBE I WAS JUST AFTER THE POWER, THE CONNECTIONS, THE MONEY...

THE MONEY...

ANYWAY, TURNS OUT HE WAS CRAP. I'M OVER IT.

P.S.—GET OFF MY STAGE.

HEY, CONGRATS, KIDS.

THEY'RE SHUTTING DOWN MY NEW FAVOURITE CLUB AFTER ONE NIGHT, BUT I'M GLAD YOU GOT YOUR CRAP SORTED OUT.

SO LIKE, WHEN YOU GUYS DISAPPEARED IN THE MIDDLE OF THE FIGHT... WHAT WAS THAT ALL ABOUT?

OH *MAN!* WE WENT IN RAMONA'S HEAD WHERE GIDEON WAS LIKE EIGHTY FEET TALL AND HOLDING HER PRISONER LIKE A TOTAL BAD DUDE!

THEN I HEADBUTTED HIM AND GAVE HIM THE GLOW AND THERE WERE A MILLION RAMONAS AND THEY KICKED HIS ASS! IT WAS *AMAZING!*

YES.

DUH, YEAH.

VERY MUCH SO.

M-ME TOO?

I'M A LITTLE CURIOUS, SURE.

DUDES, I JUST WENT TO MY DAD'S.

HE LIVES IN THE MIDDLE OF NOWHERE. I THOUGHT I'D GET MY HEAD TOGETHER AND COME BACK IN A WEEK OR TWO.

YOU KNOW, LIKE A WILDERNESS SABBATICAL.

YOU SEE, SCOTT? WILDERNESS!

YEAH, BUT IT DIDN'T REALLY WORK THAT WAY.

I JUST ENDED UP SLEEPING ALL DAY, DICKING AROUND ON THE INTERNET AND WATCHING EVERY EPISODE OF THE X-FILES. I MEAN, I *TRIED* CALLING YOU, SCOTT...

...YEAH...

...MAYBE YOU TWO WERE MEANT TO BE.

JUST CALL ME FOR THE WEDDING.

222

SO
ANYWAY

YOU WANT TO GRAB A DRINK WITH US AND CHAT?

FREAKING OUT A LOT

I—I'M FREAKING OUT A LITTLE!

OKAY, UH, YEAH, I GUESS I'M GAY. I REALIZED I LIKE DUDES.

IT SHOCKED EVERYONE WHEN I CAME OUT, BACK IN VOLUME 5. YOU SEEMED BUSY, SO I DIDN'T MENTION IT.

SO LIKE... *JULIE* TURNED YOU *GAY?!*

SERIOUSLY. GET NEW ONES.

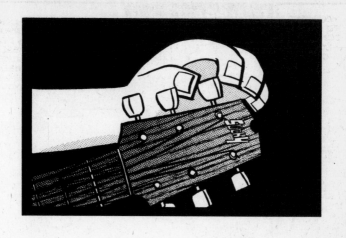

CRITICAL NOTICES

YOU GUYS ARE, UM...

YOU GUYS HAVE SO MUCH POTENTIAL!

THAT WAS AN EXTREMELY BAD COVER OF "I'M A BELIEVER" BY THE MONKEES.

BAD NEWS, SCOTT. THE ONLY TWO PEOPLE WHO COULD EVER BE OUR FANS HAVE DEVELOPED TASTE.

HELL, WHO NEEDS 'EM?

WE'LL JUST KEEP PLAYING TO YOUR CAT.

WANT TO DO IT AGAIN?

LET'S DO IT AGAIN.

234

THEN.

SO UM I MEAN I GUESS I'LL

snff

BAWL

GIVE ME A CALL WHEN YOU'RE IN TOWN, OKAY?

SCOTT...

YOU'LL ALWAYS BE MY CLASH AT DEMONHEAD.

Whatever that means.

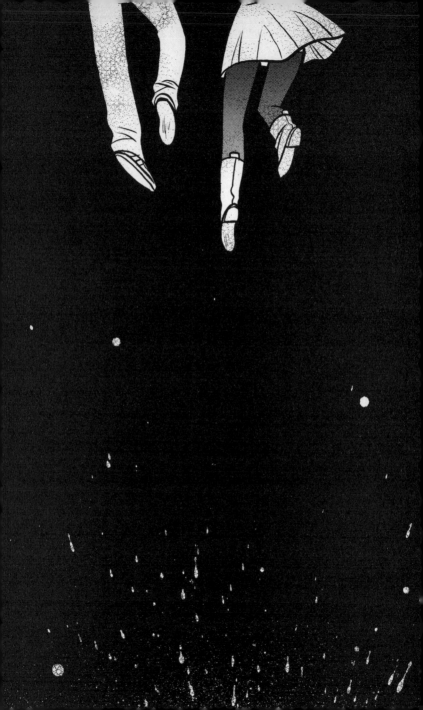

CREATED B[Y]

BRYAN LEE O'MALLE[Y]
(CREATOR — 31 YEARS OLD[)]

*Wrote and drew the book,
despite everything.*

This book and all the others and t[he]
past six years and the other years[ ]
are all dedicated to Hope Larson.

Thank you and goodnight.

Albums that got me through this:
The Cardigans - *Super Extra Gravity*; Annie - *Don't Stop,*
Neko Case - *Middle Cyclone*; Gorillaz - *Plastic Beach*;
LCD Soundsystem - *This Is Happening*; Sleigh Bells - *Treats*,
Pavement - *Quarantine the Past*; and Spoon - *Transferenc[e]*

JOHN KANTZ
Screentone, background art (28 years old)
Artist, *Legends From Darkwood*.
Designed Gideon's cryogenic apparatus.
www.jackmo.com

AARON ANCHETA
Crowd scenes, inking assist (20 years ol[d])
Student at the University of Arizona. This[ ]
is his first published work. Drew a lot of[ ]
Ramonas. *www.aancheta.com*